Finding the Party

by Jessica Quilty
illustrated by Erin Eitter-Kono

 HOUGHTON MIFFLIN HARCOURT
School Publishers

Copyright © by Houghton Mifflin Harcourt Publishing Company

Printed in China

ISBN-13: 978-0-547-02307-6
ISBN-10: 0-547-02307-3

5 6 7 8 0940 18 17 16 15 14 13 12
4500350925

It was almost time for Phil's party! Luisa was so excited.

Phil was the new kid in her class. He had invited everyone to his birthday party.

Luisa grabbed her gift and headed for the door. "Come on, Dad!" she cried. "We don't want to be late for the party!"

Luisa ran next door and rang the bell. Out came her friend Max. His little sister, Sam, was with him.

"I'm Max's assistant!" Sam said.

Max was looking at a map. "Phil gave us directions to his house. I think it's this way. What do you think?"

"That looks right," Luisa agreed.

"Let's go!" said Max.

"I know where we're going!" Sam cried as they started walking. "I know where the party is!"

"I'm glad you know where we're going," Luisa said, "but the map will show us."

"Yeah, Sam, the map won't fail us," said Max, as he and Luisa looked at it.

Soon they saw Taylor. He was in their class, too. He looked lost.

"Which way should we go?" asked Taylor.

"We know which way to go!" Luisa said.

"Do you?" asked Taylor. "The directions say that the party is on Maple. But is it Maple *Street*? Or is it Maple *Road*?"

"The map should say if it's Maple Road or Maple Street," said Max.

"Okay, but hurry!" said Taylor. "I don't want to be late!"

"This map shows both Maple Street and Maple Road. But we still don't know which one to go to!" said Max.

Sam was still jumping around.

"Stop jumping, Sam!" ordered Luisa.

Just then, Keshia came around the corner, carrying a piece of paper. She was in their class, too, and joined the group.

"Mom gave me directions," she said. "The party is on Maple."

"We know," said Max. "But is it Maple Street or Maple Road?"

"Good question," said Keshia. "I don't know."

"Let's look at the map again," said Max.
"That won't help," Luisa said.
"Maybe we should call Phil," said Keshia.
"We're going to be *really* late," said Taylor.
Sam was still jumping up and down.
"Stop jumping, Sam!" Luisa cried.

Sam was getting mad now. She waved her hands and shouted, "I can find the party! I know where to find the party!"

"Sam, it's not polite to shout," said Max.

The children put all their gifts down in a pile. They looked at the map again. They read the directions one more time. They looked at the street signs. Should they go left or right?

"ARRRGHHH!" cried Luisa.

Suddenly Sam climbed to the top of a big rock and looked around.

Then she grinned. Then she laughed. Then she pointed.

"Why are you laughing?" Max asked. "This isn't funny!"

But Sam kept pointing. Then she started jumping up and down again.

"I see the party," said Sam. "You will, too. Just walk around this rock!"

They all walked around the big rock. There it was! Phil's house was covered with balloons and other decorations. Phil was standing outside.

"Look! It's on the corner of Maple Street AND Maple Road!" Luisa said. "Thanks, Sam. You cleared up the mystery. You have more wisdom than I realized."

Max took one last look at the map that caused so much trouble before tearing it up.

"I want cake!" said Sam.

"You get the first piece!" everyone shouted.

Sam just grinned.

Responding

✔ TARGET SKILL **Text and Graphic Features** There are clues in this story's pictures. Copy the chart below. Write each page number where you can see the party house. Then write why the children miss it and how they feel.

Page Number	Reason	How They Feel
3	Looking at map	Excited
?	?	?
?	?	?

Write About It

Text to Self Write a fictional narrative paragraph about some friends who get lost. Remember to state the problem in the beginning, work on it in the middle, and solve it at the end.